Lively Aunt Lizzie

ELIZABETH BEST

Illustrated by Greg Gaul

sundance

A Haights Cross Communications Company

The Story Characters

Aunt Lizzie

Gertie

Bert

The Story Setting

TABLE OF CONTENTS

CHAPTER 1

Happy Birthday

On Aunt Lizzie's 65th birthday, she got a card.

It said, "Happy Birthday."

On the inside, the card said, "Here's how to live to be 100 years old. Live to be 99. Then be very, very careful."

"I'll do it!" cried Aunt Lizzie. "I'll live to be 100 years old! I'll find out how to be very, very careful!"

So Aunt Lizzie bought a book called
How to Be Very, Very Careful.

She opened it to page one.
The words filled the page.

"Watch what you eat!"

So she did.

Before she ate, Aunt Lizzie always put
on her glasses.

Aunt Lizzie ate cherry pies and chocolate cake. She ate lollipops and sticky buns. She ate potato chips and ice cream.

Aunt Lizzie watched all of the food as it went into her mouth.

This is going to be easy, Aunt Lizzie thought.

CHAPTER 2

No Fat and No Sugar

On page two of the book, Aunt Lizzie carefully read,

"Don't eat too much fat!"

How much is too much? Aunt Lizzie wondered. She looked at her dinner . . . four fat sausages.

"I know," she cried. "I won't eat four fat sausages. I'll eat eight thin ones."

On page three, Aunt Lizzie read,

"Don't eat too much sugar!"

How
to Be
Very,
Very
Careful

Aunt Lizzie's favorite food was chocolate cake.

Was chocolate cake full of sugar? She had to find out.

She set off for the cake shop.

The cake shop was full of people. Aunt Lizzie picked up a chocolate cake.

Aunt Lizzie stuck out her tongue and licked the cake. Yum!

"That's not sugar," she said. "That's chocolate!"

So she bought five chocolate cakes.

CHAPTER 3

Don't Overdo It

On page four of her book, she read,

"Walk a mile a day.
But . . . DON'T OVERDO IT!"

She tied a walking meter onto one leg
so she'd know when to stop. As she
walked, she listened to the meter
clicking. Walking made her feel good.

Why didn't I try this before? she thought.

Aunt Lizzie walked a mile. But she didn't turn back. She just kept going.

click click click click click click

Aunt Lizzie was lucky the first time.
After an hour, she stopped at a bus
stop. So she caught the bus home.

The second time, Aunt Lizzie went a different way. She wasn't so lucky. She had to walk home.

click

I must not overdo it, she thought.
That's one of the rules.

click

The next day, Aunt Lizzie didn't leave the house. She walked around the bedroom, up the hall, through the kitchen, and back again. She did this until the meter told her that she'd walked a mile.

Aunt Lizzie's niece, Gertie, lived in a little room in the basement. She heard footsteps and the meter clicking away like crazy.

"Aunt Lizzie," she yelled, "you've got to stop walking! Click, click, click. Thump, thump, thump. I really can't stand it."

Aunt Lizzie was very upset. "Don't you want me to live to be 100?" she cried.

Aunt Lizzie Disappears

The next day, Aunt Lizzie went to the bank. She took out all of her money. Then she took a trip around the world.

One day Gertie said, "I haven't seen
Aunt Lizzie for months."

As she ate toast and honey, Gertie thought about Aunt Lizzie. She'd never left home for this long before. Where could Aunt Lizzie be?

Gertie called her brother, Bert. "Aunt Lizzie's gone," she said.

"We'd better look for her," said Bert.

Gertie and Bert climbed into the car
and drove around the neighborhood.
They didn't find Aunt Lizzie.

Gertie and Bert put ads in the **Daily News.** They talked to the police.

But they didn't find Aunt Lizzie.

CHAPTER 5

Not So Careful

The years passed.

One day, Gertie and Bert were cleaning Aunt Lizzie's house. They heard the sound of a key in the lock.

Aunt Lizzie was back! And today was her 99th birthday!

"Happy birthday, Auntie!" they cried.
"That book must have helped you. You
must have been very, very careful."

"Yes," said Aunt Lizzie. "That book told me everything I needed to know."

As she stepped into the room, she tripped over the broom. Aunt Lizzie flung up her arms.

She was going to fall.

But Aunt Lizzie didn't fall. She leaped into the air. Then she started to dance. Down the hall and around the kitchen she danced.

Gertie and Bert ran after her.

Aunt Lizzie took a flying leap into a big, fat chair.

"You call that being careful?" they both shouted.

"Oh, I love leaping into this old chair," Aunt Lizzie said.

Then Aunt Lizzie laughed. "Hee! Hee!"
she said. "Gertie, you should read that
book of mine. You'll learn a lot."

Aunt Lizzie tossed the book onto the table for Gertie.

Gertie picked up the well-worn book. The book fell open to the last page.

Gertie read the big print.

"Have fun.
Enjoy your life!"

GLOSSARY

careful

paying lots of attention

favorite

the most liked

meter

a machine to

measure something

tossed
threw

tripped
stumbled

upset
felt sad

wondered
thought about

Elizabeth Best

Elizabeth Best writes a bit of everything . . . adult short stories, children's stories, plays, articles, and novels. Best of all, though, she enjoys writing stories for children. It is pure joy for her! Elizabeth has a pet Jack Russell terrier and hates getting out of bed in the morning.

Greg Gaul

Greg Gaul lives in the Blue Mountains with his wife, Carol, and their very old dog, Boofy. He works in his studio, where he enjoys watching the many birds that visit throughout the year. Occasionally, when working late, he is treated to the antics of a big possum in a nearby tree. Greg thinks illustrating is a great way to earn a living.

sundance
A Haights Cross Communications Company

Published by Sundance Publishing
P.O. Box 740, One Beeman Road, Northborough, MA 01532
800-343-8204

Copyright © text Elizabeth Best
Copyright © illustrations Greg Gaul

First published 1999 as Sparklers by
Blake Education, Locked Bag 2022, Glebe 2037, Australia
Exclusive United States Distribution: Sundance Publishing

ISBN 0-7608-8002-6